50 free food
feasts

INDEX
BOOKS LTD

Originally published in Great Britain in 2005
This edition published 2008 for Index Books Ltd
10 9 8 7 6 5 4 3 2 1

Ebury Publishing
Random House, 20 Vauxhall Bridge Road, London SW1V 2SA

Random House Australia (Pty) Limited
20 Alfred Street, Milsons Point, Sydney, New South Wales 2061, Australia

Random House New Zealand Limited
18 Poland Road, Glenfield, Auckland 10, New Zealand

Random House South Africa (Pty) Limited
Isle of Houghton, Corner Boundary Road & Carse O'Gowrie, Houghton, 2198, South Africa

Random House Publishers India Private Limited
301 World Trade Tower, Hotel Intercontinental Grand Complex, Barakhamba Lane, New Delhi 110 001, India

The Random House Group Limited Reg. No. 954009
www.randomhouse.co.uk

A CIP catalogue record for this book is available from the British Library.

ISBN: 978 0 09192 534 5

Recipes created by Sunil Vijayakar
Editor: Emma Callery
Design: Nicky Barneby

Food photography: Jon Whitaker
Food stylist: Sunil Vijayakar
Prop stylist: Rachel Jukes

For Slimming World
Founder and Chairman: Margaret Miles-Bramwell
Managing Director: Caryl Richards
Project co-ordinators: Allison Brentnall and Beverley Farnsworth
Text by Sheila Ashton

Papers used by Ebury Press are natural, recyclable products made
from wood grown in sustainable forests.

Printed and bound by Butler and Tanner, Frome

contents

dreams come true . . .

If you've ever longed for a health-conscious culinary 'fairy godmother' to wave a wand and guide you through the menu maze, then Slimming World's *50 free food feasts* will indeed make your dreams come true.

OK, I'm exaggerating, but if, like me, you're no magician in the kitchen, you'll be delighted by this stunning collection of deliciously satisfying recipes. Each one is quick, easy, healthy – and designed for everyday cooking in ordinary kitchens. And best of all, you'll be amazed at how much food you can make 'disappear' while losing weight beautifully!

That includes temptingly tasty dishes such as Creamy Asparagus Carbonara, Risotto or Mustard and Garlic Roasted Leg of Lamb. And how would you like to enjoy Pasta Funghi or Comfort Food Fish Pie to your heart's content?

Believe me, this is no trick. The 'secret' that lies behind the freeing power of these 50 sumptuous, hand-picked dishes is Free Food®, the proven powerhouse of Food Optimising®. Slimming World's unique eating system has already helped thousands of men and women to slim and maintain their weight and this recipe book has the power to help you too!

You can rest assured that, because you're choosing Free Foods, you can enjoy any and all of these fabulous dishes without limit and without feeling guilt, deprivation or that awful fear of losing control around food (or saucepans!). The recipes in this collection will help you to unleash the power of Free Food. With them you can satisfy your appetite any time you choose, anywhere you fancy, and still lose weight. So go ahead and explore Free Food to the full – you'll discover that it's amazingly simple and simply amazing! And doesn't that sound magic?

With love,

Margaret Miles-Bramwell
Slimming World Founder and Chairman

starters, snacks
and salads

minted green pea and basil soup

minted green pea and basil soup

A gorgeous colour and a crunchy–smooth texture with a tang of herbs make a lovely fresh soup.

SERVES 4
Preparation time
10 minutes
Cooking time
30 minutes
Green: Free

3 large shallots, finely chopped

1 garlic clove, peeled and finely chopped

4 tbsp chopped basil leaves

4 tbsp chopped mint leaves

900ml/1½ pints chicken stock made from Bovril

500g/1lb 2oz frozen or fresh peas

salt and freshly ground black pepper

to serve
very low-fat natural yogurt

to garnish
mint and basil leaves

1. Place the shallots in a medium saucepan with the garlic and chopped herbs. Pour over the stock, bring to the boil, cover, reduce the heat to medium and simmer for 10 minutes or until the shallots are tender.

2. Add the peas, bring back to the boil and cook gently for 5 minutes. Season well to taste.

3. Transfer half the mixture to a food processor and blend until smooth. Return to the pan with the remaining soup and stir to mix well.

4. Ladle the soup into bowls and serve with a swirl of the yogurt. Garnish with mint and basil leaves and serve immediately.

roasted yellow pepper soup

A super-healthy soup, ideal for a summer lunch. Don't worry about the amount of garlic; it adds a rich depth to the flavour when cooked.

SERVES 4

Preparation time
10 minutes

Cooking time
50 minutes

Green/Original: Free

6 large yellow peppers

10 ripe plum tomatoes

6 whole garlic cloves

2 tbsp light soy sauce

2 tbsp chopped basil leaves

salt and freshly ground black pepper

to garnish
basil leaves

1. Preheat the oven to 200°C/Gas 6. Halve and deseed the peppers and place on a non-stick baking sheet and roast for 15 minutes.

2. Halve the tomatoes and add to the peppers with the garlic cloves and roast for a further 25–30 minutes.

3. Remove from the oven and carefully peel the skin off the peppers and discard. Place the peeled peppers in a food processor with the plum tomatoes.

4. Squeeze the garlic from their skins into the processor with the soy sauce and chopped basil leaves. Add 300ml/12fl oz hot water and process until smooth.

5. Transfer the mixture to a saucepan and place over a medium heat. Bring to the boil, remove from the heat and season well before serving, ladled into warmed soup plates or bowls and garnished with the basil leaves.

roasted stuffed aubergines

A classic flavouring of cinnamon and coriander brings out the full smoky sweetness of roasted aubergine, and the couscous and chickpeas make this a very satisfying Green day meal.

SERVES 4

Preparation time
20 minutes

Cooking time
40 minutes

Green: Free

100g/4oz couscous

2 medium aubergines

6 spring onions, trimmed and finely sliced

4 tbsp chopped coriander leaves

2 plum tomatoes, finely chopped

1 x 400g/14oz can chickpeas, rinsed and drained

1 tsp ground cinnamon

salt and freshly ground black pepper

1. Preheat the oven to 220°C/Gas 7. Place the couscous in a heatproof bowl and pour over enough boiling water to only just cover. Cover and leave to stand for 10 minutes. Fluff up the couscous grains with a fork and set aside.

2. Meanwhile, halve the aubergines lengthways and, using a sharp-edged teaspoon, carefully scoop out the aubergine flesh from the centre, leaving the skin intact to form a shell.

3. Finely chop the scooped out flesh and mix into the prepared couscous with the spring onions, coriander leaves, tomatoes, chickpeas and cinnamon. Season well.

4. Pack the couscous mixture into each aubergine shell. Place on a non-stick baking sheet, cover with foil and place in the oven and roast for 25 minutes. Remove the foil and cook for a further 10–15 minutes or until the aubergines have collapsed slightly and are tender. Serve immediately with a crisp green salad if desired.

cumin-scented chickpea falafels

Middle Eastern spices such as cumin and ginger add a fragrant lightness to these chunky, savoury, bite-sized burgers. Great for parties or for serving with couscous and roasted vegetables as a main meal.

SERVES 4

Preparation time
20 minutes + chilling

Cooking time
20 minutes

Green: Free

1 onion, peeled and finely chopped

1 carrot, peeled and coarsely grated

2 x 400g/14oz can chickpeas, rinsed and drained

2 garlic cloves, peeled and finely chopped

1 tsp finely grated ginger

2 tsp ground cumin

1 tsp chilli powder

1 tsp ground coriander

3 tbsp very finely chopped fresh coriander leaves

1 small egg

salt

Fry Light for spraying

to serve
very low-fat natural yogurt

1. Place the onion, carrot, chickpeas, garlic, ginger, cumin, chilli powder and the ground and fresh coriander in a food processor. Pulse and process for 1–2 minutes or until blended but still fairly chunky in texture.

2. Transfer the mixture to a mixing bowl. Lightly beat the egg and add to the mixture. Season with salt and, using your fingers, mix thoroughly to combine. Cover and chill in the fridge for 6–8 hours, or overnight, to firm up and allow the flavours to develop.

3. Preheat the oven to 200°C/Gas 6. Line a large baking sheet with non-stick baking parchment and spray lightly with Fry Light. Shape the chickpea mixture into bite-sized balls and place on the prepared baking sheet. Spray lightly with Fry Light and cook in the oven for 15–20 minutes or until lightly golden and firm. Serve warm, with the yogurt to dip into.

tuscan sardine pâté
with vegetable crudités

Whip up a home-made sardine pâté in minutes – served with chunky vegetable sticks it makes a very healthy starter or snack.

SERVES 4
Preparation time
15 minutes + chilling

Original: Free

2 x 120g/4½oz cans sardines in tomato sauce
250g/9oz Quark soft cheese
finely grated zest and juice of 1 lemon
salt and freshly ground black pepper
2 tbsp capers

6 tbsp finely chopped flat-leaf parsley

for the crudités
1 large carrot
4 sticks celery
1 red pepper

1. Place the sardines in a mixing bowl. Add the Quark and, using a fork, stir to combine. Add the lemon zest and juice and stir to mix well. Season to taste.

2. Rinse and drain the capers and add to the sardine mixture together with the chopped parsley. Mix the ingredients together until fairly well combined. Alternatively, for a smoother pâté, place all the ingredients in a food processor and blend until smooth.

3. Transfer the pâté to a serving bowl or a couple of individual ramekins, cover with cling film and allow to chill in the fridge for 3–4 hours to let the flavours steadily develop.

4. Meanwhile, peel the carrots and cut them and the celery into dipping-size sticks. Deseed the red pepper and cut into thick strips. To serve, place the sardine pâté on a platter surrounded by the vegetable crudités.

chicken and herb balls

The mixture of herbs and spices in these bite-sized chicken balls ensures that each one just bursts with flavour – fantastic to serve at parties or with pre-dinner drinks.

SERVES 4
Preparation time
10 minutes + chilling
Cooking time
20 minutes
Original: Free

4 spring onions, trimmed and very finely chopped
2 garlic cloves, peeled and crushed
500g/1lb 2oz lean chicken mince
1 red chilli, deseeded and very finely chopped
1 tsp ground ginger
1 tsp ground cumin
1 tsp ground coriander
2 tbsp very finely chopped coriander leaves
2 tbsp very finely chopped mint leaves
salt and freshly ground black pepper

to serve
very low-fat natural fromage frais (optional)
lime wedges

1. Place the spring onions, garlic, chicken mince, red chilli, ground spices and chopped herbs into a mixing bowl. Season and, using your fingers, mix thoroughly. Cover and chill for 3–4 hours.

2. Preheat the oven to 200°C/Gas 6. Line a large baking sheet with non-stick baking parchment.

3. Divide the mixture into 16 portions and then shape each portion into a ball. Place the balls on the prepared baking sheet and place in the oven for 20 minutes or until cooked through. Remove from the oven and serve hot, accompanied with a very low-fat natural fromage frais dip, if desired, and lime wedges.

smoked trout parcels

These pretty pink and green parcels are easy to make ahead for a light dinner party starter; the secret ingredient is the lime zest, which gives an extra-fresh zing. Add a little caviare for a super-luxurious touch!

SERVES 4

Preparation time
20 minutes

Original: Free

100g/4oz Quark soft cheese

2 tbsp very finely chopped dill

2 tbsp very finely snipped chives

1 tsp very finely grated lime zest

1 garlic clove, peeled and crushed

salt and freshly ground black pepper

8 x 25g/1oz slices smoked trout

long chives

to garnish

very low-fat natural fromage frais

salmon roe or caviare

dill sprigs

1. Place the Quark in a small bowl. Add the chopped dill and chives with the lime zest and garlic. Season and mix well to combine.

2. Lay the smoked trout slices on a clean work surface and spoon the Quark mixture into the centre of each one. Carefully roll up the slices to form neat parcels and, using long chives, tie up the parcels to form 'presents'.

3. Chill until ready to serve and then place small spoonfuls of fromage frais on top of each parcel and garnish with salmon roe or caviare and sprigs of dill.

garlic and chilli dip
with crispy potato skins

Perfect for a 'big night in' for entertaining, or just when you deserve a comfort-food snack. The cool, creamy dip makes a fantastic contrast with the hot, crispy potatoes.

SERVES 4

Preparation time
15 minutes

Cooking time
1 hour 5 minutes

Green: Free

for the potato skins
4 jacket potatoes
Fry Light for spraying
sea salt

for the dip
250g/9oz very low-fat natural fromage frais

4 garlic cloves, peeled and crushed
2 red chillies, deseeded and very finely chopped
2 tsp lemon juice
3 tbsp finely chopped dill
2 tbsp chopped parsley
salt

1. Preheat the oven to 200°C/Gas 6. Prick the potatoes all over with a skewer or prongs of a fork and place on a non-stick baking sheet. Spray with Fry Light and sprinkle over some sea salt. Bake in the oven for 1 hour or until the centres of the potatoes are tender.

2. Remove from the oven, cut the potatoes in half and, using a spoon, scoop out most of the flesh and save for another recipe, leaving a thin layer of potato around the inside of each shell.

3. Using a sharp knife, cut the potato halves into half again, making 16 potato skins. Place back onto the baking sheet and return to the oven for 5 minutes.

4. Meanwhile, make the dip by combining all the ingredients in a small bowl and mixing well. Remove the potato skins from the oven and serve immediately with the cool, creamy garlic, dill and chilli dip.

herbed couscous salad

Couscous lends itself to all kinds of different flavours; here it is teamed with a citrusy, spicy dressing, crunchy vegetables and a handful of fresh herbs.

SERVES 4

Preparation time

15 minutes

Green: Free

250g/9oz couscous

1 cucumber, finely diced

4 plum tomatoes, roughly chopped

1 red onion, peeled and finely diced

6 tbsp chopped coriander leaves

6 tbsp chopped mint leaves

for the dressing

finely grated zest and juice of 1 lemon

1 tsp ground cumin

1 garlic clove, peeled and crushed

60ml/2fl oz chicken stock made from Bovril

1 red chilli, deseeded and finely sliced

salt

1. Place the couscous in a large bowl and pour over boiling hot water to just cover. Cover with a lid and let stand for 10–12 minutes.

2. Meanwhile, place the cucumber, tomatoes and onion in a large salad bowl together with the chopped herbs. Fluff up the grains of the couscous with a fork and add to the salad ingredients. Mix well.

3. Make the dressing by mixing together the lemon zest and juice, cumin, garlic, stock and red chilli. Season with salt and stir to mix well.

4. Pour the dressing over the couscous salad, toss to mix well and serve at room temperature.

wild rice
and carrot salad

Rice salad is very versatile; it travels well on picnics or in lunchboxes and is always popular at a party buffet. This recipe features the added crunch of wild rice and is full of colour as well as flavour.

SERVES 4
Preparation time
15 minutes
Cooking time
10 minutes

Green: Free

200g/7oz mixed wild and Basmati rice

salt

2 carrots, peeled and cut into matchsticks

200g/7oz green beans, halved lengthways

2 ripe plum tomatoes, roughly chopped

1 red onion, peeled, halved and thinly sliced

200g/7oz canned sweetcorn niblets, rinsed and drained

4 tbsp fat-free French-style salad dressing

1. Cook the rice according to the packet instructions. Drain and rinse in cold water to cool. Drain again, shaking off any excess water, and place the rice in a large shallow salad bowl.

2. Bring a large pan of lightly salted water to the boil. Add the carrots and beans and cook for 3 minutes before draining and rinsing under cold water to cool.

3. Add the carrots and beans to the rice with the chopped tomatoes, red onion and sweetcorn.

4. Pour over the dressing and toss the salad ingredients to mix well. Serve immediately.

tuna, capers
and mixed grilled pepper salad

Capers have a uniquely tangy taste that brings out the flavour in other ingredients – in this case, a super-healthy salad of tuna and roasted mixed peppers that's easily made in advance.

SERVES 4

Preparation time
10 minutes

Cooking time
10–12 minutes

Original: Free

8 mixed peppers (red, orange and yellow)

1 red onion

1 garlic clove, peeled and finely grated

juice of 1 lemon

2 x 200g/7oz cans tuna in brine, drained

3 tbsp capers or caperberries

½ small cucumber, cut into thin strips

salt and freshly ground black pepper

to serve

100g/4oz bag of wild rocket leaves

1. Halve and deseed the peppers, place them skin side up under a hot grill and cook for 10–12 minutes until the skin is blackened and charred. Remove and place in a plastic bag for 10–12 minutes. When cool, peel and cut into strips and place in a bowl with any saved juices.

2. Halve the onion, peel and thinly slice and add to the peppers with the garlic and lemon juice.

3. Flake the tuna into large chunks and add to the pepper mixture with the capers and cucumber. Season well and toss to mix. To serve, divide the rocket leaves between four plates and top with the tuna mixture.

minted tropical fruit salad

The perfect end to a meal, a tropical fruit salad spiked with mint is super-healthy, very refreshing and is easily made in advance and left to chill.

SERVES 4
Preparation time
25 minutes
Green/Original: Free

3 ripe mangoes
8 large kiwi fruit
½ small green melon
1 small honeydew melon

250g/9oz watermelon wedge, seeds removed

to serve
a handful of fresh mint leaves

1. Cut the cheeks off the sides of the mangoes and, using a melon baller, make balls of the mango flesh and place in a bowl. Cut the kiwi fruit in half and, using the melon baller again, repeat and add the kiwi balls to the mangoes.

2. Halve the melon and deseed. Repeat the procedure with the melon baller to give you melon and watermelon balls.

3. Divide the mixed fruit balls between four dessert bowls and scatter over the mint leaves. Serve chilled.

duck, mango and watercress salad

Peppery watercress, sweet mango, rich duck breast and crunchy red pepper combine in a luxurious salad with a tropical, Oriental tang.

SERVES 4

Preparation time
15 minutes
Cooking time
16 minutes

Original: Free

salt and freshly ground black pepper

4 skinless duck breasts, trimmed of all visible fat

Fry Light for spraying

2 ripe sweet mangoes

4 spring onions, trimmed and shredded

1 red pepper, deseeded and very thinly sliced

a large bunch of watercress

for the dressing

4 tbsp light soy sauce

1 tsp Chinese five-spice powder

1 tbsp Worcestershire sauce

1 tsp Tabasco sauce

60ml/2fl oz chicken stock made from Bovril

1. Season the duck breasts well and spray with Fry Light. Place on a grill rack under a medium–hot grill and cook for 6–8 minutes on each side or until cooked to your liking. Remove from the grill, cover with foil and allow to rest for 10 minutes.

2. Meanwhile, peel, stone and cut the mangoes into bite-sized cubes and place in a large bowl with the spring onions, red pepper and watercress. Toss to mix well.

3. To serve, divide the salad mixture between four serving plates. Thinly slice the duck and place on top of the salad. Mix together all the dressing ingredients and serve the salad with the dressing spooned over.

meat and poultry

chicken tikka masala

chicken tikka masala

Your local Indian restaurant will wonder what's happened to you once you've discovered this fantastic home-made version of a classic dish that's Free on Original days.

SERVES 4
Preparation time
20 minutes
Cooking time
25 minutes
Original: Free

4 chicken breast fillets, skinned
Fry Light for spraying
salt and freshly ground black pepper
2 large shallots, peeled
3 garlic cloves, peeled
½ tsp crushed cardamom seeds
½ tsp turmeric
1 tbsp tikka masala powder or tandoori spice blend powder

4 tbsp passata
150ml/5fl oz chicken stock made from Bovril
100g/4oz very low-fat natural fromage frais

to serve
very low-fat natural fromage frais
chopped fresh coriander leaves
lime wedges (optional)

1. Spray the chicken with Fry Light, season and place under a hot grill and cook for 15–16 minutes, turning once until cooked through. Remove and, when cool, cut into bite-sized pieces. Set aside.

2. Using a fine grater, grate the shallots and garlic into a bowl. Spray a large non-stick frying pan with Fry Light and place over a medium heat. Add the shallot and garlic mixture with the crushed cardamom seeds, turmeric and tikka masala powder. Stir-fry for 1 minute before adding the passata.

3. Add the chicken and stock and cook for 4–5 minutes, stirring often. Add the fromage frais, season to taste and remove from the heat. Drizzle over a little fromage frais, garnish with chopped coriander and lime wedges, if desired, and serve with steamed cabbage or any other Free vegetables of your choice.

mediterranean chicken hot pot

Slow-cooking the chicken and vegetables in this casserole creates a deliciously fragrant, meltingly tender dish that will become an instant 'all-time favourite'.

SERVES 4
Preparation time
20 minutes
Cooking time
1 hour 45 minutes

Original: Free

6 large chicken breast fillets, skinned
1 x 400g/14oz can tomatoes
3 garlic cloves, peeled and finely chopped
6 shallots
1 red pepper
1 yellow pepper
2 courgettes
200g/7oz mushrooms

1 tsp dried mixed herbs
1 tbsp artificial sweetener
700ml/24fl oz chicken stock made from Bovril
salt and freshly ground black pepper

to serve
a large handful of fresh basil leaves

1. Preheat the oven to 200°C/Gas 6. Cut the chicken into bite-sized pieces and place in a medium casserole dish with the canned tomatoes.

2. Add the garlic to the chicken mixture. Halve and peel the shallots, deseed the peppers and cut into bite-sized pieces and add to the casserole dish.

3. Thickly slice the courgettes and mushrooms and add to the chicken mixture with the dried mixed herbs, artificial sweetener and chicken stock. Place the casserole dish over a high heat and bring to the boil. Cover very tightly and place in the oven and cook for 1½ hours.

4. Remove from the oven, season well and stir in the fresh basil leaves just before serving.

sweet and sour chicken

Enjoy the flavours of sweet and sour chicken without the sticky heaviness of a restaurant version – it's just as quick as a takeaway too.

SERVES 4

Preparation time
15 minutes +
marinating
Cooking time
10 minutes

Original: Free

6 chicken breast fillets, skinned

6 spring onions, trimmed and finely sliced

2 garlic cloves, peeled and finely chopped

salt and freshly ground black pepper

3 tbsp light soy sauce

Fry Light for spraying

1 tbsp dark soy sauce

2 tbsp artificial sweetener

2 tbsp raspberry vinegar

1 tsp paprika

½ tsp Chinese five-spice powder

100ml/3½fl oz passata

1. Slice the chicken very thinly and place in a shallow, non-reactive dish. Sprinkle over the spring onions and garlic, season well and pour over the light soy sauce. Toss to mix well, cover and marinate in the fridge for 30 minutes.

2. Spray a large, non-stick frying pan with Fry Light and, when hot, add the chicken mixture and cook over a high heat. Stir and cook for 5–6 minutes and then add all of the remaining ingredients.

3. Stir to mix well and bring the mixture to the boil. Reduce the heat and cook gently for 3–4 minutes or until the chicken is cooked through. Check seasoning and serve immediately.

moroccan lamb koftas

This is a traditional dish that offers an exotic and delicious mixture of flavours and textures. The sweet sharpness of the lemons blends beautifully with the spices and the richness of the lamb.

SERVES 4

Preparation time
20 minutes

Cooking time
25 minutes

Original: Free

1 red onion, peeled and finely chopped

1kg/2lb 4oz extra lean minced lamb

3 tsp ground cumin

2 tsp ground coriander

2 tsp ground cinnamon

2 tsp ground ginger

2 tsp chilli powder

salt and freshly ground black pepper

3 preserved lemons, roughly chopped

700ml/23fl oz chicken stock made from Bovril

to serve
a handful of chopped fresh coriander leaves

1. Place the onion in a large mixing bowl with the lamb and 1 tsp each of the ground spices. Season well and, using your fingers, mix well to combine. Using wet hands, shape the mixture into walnut-sized balls and set aside.

2. Place the remaining ground spices in a medium, non-stick saucepan with the preserved lemons and the stock and bring to the boil. Cover tightly, reduce the heat and simmer for 3–4 minutes.

3. Carefully add the meatballs to the saucepan, cover the pan and let simmer gently for 15–20 minutes, turning them often until cooked through. Check seasoning.

4. To serve, ladle into four warmed soup plates or bowls and sprinkle over the chopped coriander leaves.

mustard and garlic-roasted
leg of lamb

Rosemary is a classic flavouring for roast lamb, and here it receives a further boost with mustard and garlic. Perfect for a special Sunday lunch.

SERVES 4–6
Preparation time
15 minutes
Cooking time
1 hour 30 minutes + resting

Original: Free

1 small leg of lamb, weighing about 3kg/6lb 12oz and trimmed of all visible fat

3 tbsp mustard powder

10 garlic cloves, peeled

rosemary sprigs

sea salt and freshly ground black pepper

1. Preheat the oven to 230°C/Gas 8. Rub the leg of lamb all over with the mustard powder. Cut each garlic clove into 3–4 long slivers and, using a short sharp knife, stud the flesh of the lamb all over with the garlic and small sprigs of rosemary. Season liberally with salt and freshly ground black pepper.

2. Place in a roasting tin and put in the oven for 10–12 minutes per 450g/1lb for rare lamb or 15 minutes per 450g/1lb for medium.

3. After the first 15 minutes, reduce the heat to 180°C/Gas 4. Baste the meat from time to time with the pan juices.

4. When cooked, remove from the oven and allow the lamb to rest, covered in foil, in a warm place for 15–20 minutes before carving and serving with any Free vegetables of your choice.

curried pork brochettes
with mango salsa

A fresh, fruity mango salsa is the ideal accompaniment to these spicy brochettes, which have a double kick of fresh chilli and curry powder.

SERVES 4

Preparation time
20 minutes + chilling

Cooking time
10 minutes

Original: Free

1 red chilli, deseeded and finely chopped

6 spring onions, trimmed and finely sliced

900g/2lb extra lean pork mince

2 tbsp medium or hot curry powder

3 tbsp finely chopped mint leaves

50g/2oz very low-fat natural yogurt

finely grated zest and juice of 1 lime

salt and freshly ground black pepper

for the salsa

1 ripe mango, peeled, stoned and finely diced

1 bottled roasted red pepper, drained and finely diced

2 tbsp chopped coriander leaves

2 tbsp chopped mint leaves

1. Place the chilli, spring onions, pork, curry powder, mint leaves, yogurt and lime zest and juice in a bowl and mix well using your fingers. Season to taste, cover and chill for 2–3 hours in the fridge.

2. Meanwhile, make the salsa by combining all the ingredients in a bowl, toss to mix well and cover and store in the fridge until ready to serve. If you're using bamboo skewers, put eight of them into a bowl of water to soak.

3. Preheat the grill to high. Divide the mince mixture into 32 portions and shape each one into a smallish ball. Thread four balls onto each skewer and cook under the preheated grill for 4–5 minutes on each side or until cooked through. Serve immediately accompanied by the salsa.

breakfast hash
with eggs

There's nothing better than a 'full English' breakfast and this version will set you up for whatever the day has in store – hard to believe it's Free on Original days!

SERVES 4

Preparation time
20 minutes

Cooking time
30 minutes

Original: Free

6 Quorn sausages

Fry Light for spraying

2 onions, peeled and roughly chopped

250g/9oz button mushrooms, roughly chopped

300g/11oz cherry tomatoes

6 rashers of lean bacon, trimmed of all visible fat

salt and freshly ground black pepper

4 eggs

1. Preheat the oven to 200°C/Gas 6. Line two baking sheets with non-stick baking parchment. On one tray place the sausages, spray with Fry Light and place in the oven.

2. Arrange the onions, mushrooms, cherry tomatoes and bacon on the second baking sheet, spray with Fry Light and season well. Ten minutes after the sausages have gone in, place the tray with the onions, mushrooms, cherry tomatoes and bacon in the oven and cook for 20 minutes.

3. Meanwhile, cook the eggs to your liking by frying them in a non-stick frying pan lightly sprayed with Fry Light. Keep warm.

4. Remove the sausages from the oven and roughly chop. Transfer to a bowl, remove the onion tray from the oven and add the onions, mushrooms and cherry tomatoes to the sausage mixture. Roughly chop the bacon and add to the bowl. Stir to mix well.

5. To serve, divide the hash between four warmed plates and top each one with a fried egg.

spicy beef and vegetable stew

A touch of curry gives an intriguing extra bite to a classic British winter stew of beef and bacon. This is a really 'friendly' dish that will wait happily for you in the oven.

SERVES 4

Preparation time
20 minutes

Cooking time
3 hours 15 minutes

Original: Free

Fry Light for spraying

2 onions, peeled and finely chopped

800ml/28fl oz beef stock made from Bovril

600g/1lb 6oz extra lean stewing steak, cut into cubes

4 carrots, peeled and thickly sliced

2 sprigs of thyme

1 bay leaf

1 tbsp medium curry powder

1 leek, cleaned and thinly sliced

2 tbsp chopped parsley

4 rashers of lean bacon, chopped

salt and freshly ground black pepper

1. Preheat the oven to 160°C/Gas 3. Spray a large non-stick frying pan with Fry Light and add the onions. Stir-fry over a medium heat for 3–4 minutes and then add 4–5 tbsp of the stock and continue to stir and cook for 4–5 minutes or until soft. Transfer to a medium-sized casserole dish and set aside.

2. Wipe out the frying pan with kitchen paper and re-spray with Fry Light. Place over a high heat and, when hot, add the meat.

3. Stir and fry for 4–5 minutes or until the meat is sealed. Transfer to the casserole dish with any of the pan juices.

4. Add all the remaining ingredients to the casserole dish, season well, cover tightly and bake in the oven for 3 hours. Remove from the oven, check seasoning and serve immediately.

crusted fillet steak
with roast vegetable salsa

The hot, smoky taste of a grilled peppered steak is a perfect match for tender, sweet, roasted Mediterranean vegetables – well worth the time it takes to prepare the peppers, courgette, aubergine and onion.

SERVES 4

Preparation time

25 minutes +
marinating

Cooking time

45 minutes

Original: Free

2 tbsp mixed peppercorns, roughly crushed

1 tbsp Worcestershire sauce

4 fillet steaks, trimmed of all visible fat

for the vegetables

1 red pepper, deseeded and diced

1 yellow pepper, deseeded and diced

1 courgette, trimmed and diced

½ aubergine, trimmed and diced

1 red onion, peeled and diced

Fry Light for spraying

salt and freshly ground black pepper

2 tbsp chopped rosemary leaves

1. Preheat the oven to 200°C/Gas 6. Mix together the crushed peppercorns and the Worcestershire sauce. Spread this mixture over the steaks, cover and allow to marinate for 3–4 hours.

2. Prepare the vegetables and place on a large roasting tray lined with baking parchment. Spray with Fry Light, season well and sprinkle over the rosemary. Place in the oven and cook for 15–20 minutes or until the vegetables are tender and slightly charred at the edges. Remove and keep warm.

3. Meanwhile, heat a ridged non-stick griddle pan until hot. Spray the steaks with Fry Light and then cook for 3–4 minutes on each side or until cooked to your liking.

4. Remove from the pan and allow to rest for 5 minutes before serving with the roasted vegetables. Accompany with steamed green beans, if desired.

grilled tandoori duck

Giving duck a spicy tandoori coating complements the richness of the meat very well and tenderises it too. So when you grill it, it will have a melt-in-the-mouth texture.

SERVES 4
Preparation time
10 minutes +
marinating
Cooking time
15 minutes
Original: Free

4 boneless, skinless duck breasts
salt and freshly ground black pepper
8 tbsp very low-fat natural yogurt
2 tbsp tandoori spice blend powder
2 garlic cloves, peeled and crushed
2 tsp finely grated ginger
juice of 1 lemon

1 tbsp artificial sweetener
6 tbsp passata

to garnish
chopped fresh coriander and mint leaves

to serve
chopped tomato and cucumber salad

1. Place the duck breasts on a clean work surface and, using a short, sharp knife, make three or four diagonal slits in each breast. Season the breasts well and place in a single layer in a shallow, non-reactive dish.

2. In a small bowl, mix together the yogurt, tandoori spice blend, garlic, ginger, lemon juice, sweetener and passata. Pour this mixture over the duck and toss to coat evenly. Cover and marinate in the fridge overnight for the flavours to develop.

3. To cook, preheat a grill to medium–high. Place the duck breasts on a foil-lined grill rack and place about 7–8cm/3–3½in under the grill. Cook for 5–6 minutes on each side or until cooked to your liking. Serve immediately, garnished with the coriander and mint leaves and serve with a chopped tomato and cucumber salad.

fish and seafood

courgette and prawn curry

courgette and prawn curry

This is a light and colourful curry, ideal for a summer's evening, with lots of juicy flavours and interesting textures – and all cooked in one pan.

SERVES 4

Preparation time
15 minutes
Cooking time
20 minutes
Original: Free

1 medium onion, peeled and finely diced

2 garlic cloves, peeled and crushed

1 tsp finely grated ginger

1 tsp mild chilli powder

2 tsp mild curry powder

200ml/7fl oz chicken stock made with Bovril

1 large courgette

6 cherry tomatoes, halved

200ml/7fl oz passata

600g/1lb 6oz cooked, peeled tiger prawns

200g/7oz very low-fat natural fromage frais

6 tbsp very finely chopped coriander leaves

2 tbsp chopped mint leaves

salt

1. Place the onion in a medium-sized non-stick saucepan with the garlic, ginger, chilli powder, curry powder and stock. Bring to the boil over a medium heat, cover, reduce the heat to low and cook gently for 3–4 minutes.

2. Cut the courgette into thick matchsticks and add to the pan with the tomatoes and passata. Bring back to the boil and simmer gently for 10 minutes, stirring often.

3. Stir in the prawns, fromage frais and chopped herbs, season with salt and remove the pan from the heat.

4. Serve immediately with steamed green vegetables and salad.

mexican-style prawn and pepper stir-fry

Cayenne and lime add a hot, fresh flavour to this dish of chunky prawns with sweet, tender peppers and tomatoes.

SERVES 4
Preparation time
15 minutes
Cooking time
25 minutes

Original: Free

Fry Light for spraying

3 garlic cloves, peeled and thinly sliced

8 spring onions, trimmed and thinly sliced

2 tsp ground cumin

1 tsp cayenne pepper

3 mixed peppers (red, orange and yellow), deseeded and thinly sliced

1 x 400g/14oz can chopped tomatoes

1 tbsp red wine vinegar

150ml/5fl oz chicken stock made from Bovril

2 tbsp artificial sweetener

900g/2lb raw tiger prawns

juice of 1 lime

salt and freshly ground black pepper

1. Heat a large non-stick wok or frying pan sprayed with Fry Light over a medium heat. Add the garlic and spring onion, and stir and cook for 2–3 minutes.

2. Stir in the ground cumin, cayenne, mixed peppers, tomatoes, red wine vinegar, stock and sweetener. Bring to the boil, reduce the heat and cook for 12–15 minutes, stirring occasionally to prevent sticking.

3. Shell, devein and clean the prawns and add to the tomato mixture. Cook over a high heat for 4–5 minutes or until the prawns turn pink and are just cooked through. Remove from the heat, squeeze over the lime juice, season and serve immediately.

seafood and dill omelette

An everyday omelette becomes a luxurious treat in minutes with the addition of seafood and a sprinkling of herbs and spices.

SERVES 4
Preparation time
15 minutes
Cooking time
15 minutes
Original: Free

400g/14oz pack of luxury cooked mixed seafood (prawns, squid, mussels, etc.)
juice of 1 lemon
4 spring onions, trimmed and thinly sliced
salt and freshly ground black pepper

6 large eggs
2 tbsp Worcestershire sauce
4 tbsp finely chopped fresh dill
Fry Light for spraying

1. Place the seafood in a bowl with the lemon juice and spring onions. Season and toss to mix well.

2. Place the eggs in a large bowl and lightly beat in the Worcestershire sauce and dill. Season. Spray a large non-stick frying pan with Fry Light and place over a medium heat. Pour in the eggs and swirl the mixture around to evenly coat the pan.

3. Sprinkle the seafood mixture onto the surface and reduce the heat, cover and cook gently for 8–10 minutes or until the omelette is just set and the base is golden.

4. Remove from the heat and serve straight from the pan, cut into wedges and accompanied with a big salad.

tomato and monkfish kebabs

The firm flesh of monkfish makes it ideal for adding to colourful kebabs to cook on the barbecue or on the grill.

SERVES 4

Preparation time

15 minutes + marinating

Cooking time

15 minutes

Original: Free

1kg/2lb 4oz monkfish tails

200g/7oz very low-fat natural yogurt

finely grated zest and juice of 1 lime

1 tbsp dried mixed herbs

1 tbsp Worcestershire sauce

2 tsp garlic salt

1 tsp celery salt

freshly ground black pepper

16 cherry tomatoes

Fry Light for spraying

1. Skin and remove the thin membrane from the monkfish tails. Cut the fish into bite-sized cubes. Place in a single layer in a shallow, non-reactive dish.

2. Mix together the yogurt, lime zest and juice, dried herbs, Worcestershire sauce, garlic salt and celery salt and season well with freshly ground black pepper. Mix thoroughly and pour this mixture over the fish. Toss to coat evenly, cover and allow to marinate for 3–4 hours.

3. When ready to cook, turn the grill to medium–high. Thread the marinated fish pieces alternately with the cherry tomatoes onto eight metal skewers. Place on a foil-lined grill rack and spray with Fry Light. Grill for 6–7 minutes on each side or until cooked through and lightly coloured. Serve immediately.

cod cakes
with tartare sauce

These are very special fishcakes – made with cod fillet and tiger prawns, and flavoured with a subtle mix of herbs and spices. Using celeriac instead of potato ensures they are Free on Original days.

SERVES 4
Preparation time
20 minutes + chilling
Cooking time
30 minutes

Original: Free

300g/11oz celeriac
2 garlic cloves, peeled and crushed
4 spring onions, trimmed and thinly sliced
a dash of Tabasco sauce
5 tbsp very finely chopped dill
2 tsp finely grated lemon zest
250g/9oz cod fillet, skinned
100g/4oz raw tiger prawns, cleaned
½ small egg, beaten
salt and freshly ground black pepper

Fry Light for spraying

for the tartare sauce
4 small red shallots, very finely diced
2 tbsp capers
4 tbsp chopped gherkins
1 plum tomato, deseeded and roughly chopped
200g/7oz very low-fat natural yogurt
salt and freshly ground black pepper

1. Peel and cut the celeriac into small pieces and boil in lightly salted water for 8–10 minutes until tender. Drain thoroughly and place in a food processor. Stir in the garlic, spring onions, Tabasco, dill and lemon zest. Roughly chop the cod and the prawns and add to the mixture in the processor with the beaten egg. Season and process until fairly smooth.

2. Transfer to a bowl, cover and chill for 3–4 hours or overnight for the mixture to firm up and to allow the flavours to develop.

3. Preheat the oven to 200°C/Gas 6. Line a large baking sheet with non-stick baking parchment. Divide the fish mixture into eight portions and shape each into a ball. Flatten to form 'cakes' and place on the baking sheet. Spray with Fry Light and bake in the oven for 15–20 minutes or until cooked through.

4. While the cakes are cooking make the sauce by combining all the ingredients in a bowl, season well and chill until ready to serve. Serve the cod cakes warm with the sauce spooned over.

spicy grilled sardines
with mint and cucumber raita

Sardines are an oily fish that contain essential fatty acids – an important part of a healthy diet. Here they are teamed with eastern spices and a cooling raita; imagine you've just caught and cooked them on the beach!

SERVES 4
Preparation time
15 minutes + chilling
Cooking time
10 minutes

Original: Free

for the raita

1 cucumber, finely diced

2 tomatoes, finely diced

1 small red onion, peeled and finely diced

6 tbsp chopped mint leaves

200g/7oz very low-fat natural yogurt

salt and freshly ground black pepper

for the sardines

12 sardines, gutted and cleaned

juice of 2 lemons

1 tsp hot chilli powder

1 tsp ground cumin

1 tsp ground coriander

Fry Light for spraying

to serve

mint sprigs

1. Make the raita by putting all the ingredients into a bowl. Mix well, season, cover and chill until ready to use.

2. Place the sardines in a shallow, non-reactive dish, in a single layer. Mix together the lemon juice, chilli powder, ground cumin and ground coriander. Season well with salt and spoon this mixture over the sardines. Cover and chill for 15–20 minutes.

3. When ready to cook, preheat the grill to hot. Place the sardines in a single layer on a large grill rack, spray with Fry Light and cook under the grill for 4–5 minutes on each side or until cooked through and lightly charred. Serve immediately garnished with mint sprigs and the raita in a bowl alongside.

poached halibut
in cucumber sauce

Halibut is a delicately flavoured fish that lends itself very well to a fresh, savoury cucumber sauce.

SERVES 4

Preparation time

15 minutes

Cooking time

15 minutes

Original: Free

4 halibut fillets (approximately 250g/9oz each), skinned

for the sauce

150g/5oz cucumber, very finely diced

1 small onion, peeled and finely diced

600ml/1 pint chicken stock made from Bovril

4 tbsp chopped fresh dill

2 tbsp finely chopped chives

1 green chilli, deseeded and very finely chopped

salt and freshly ground black pepper

to garnish

lime wedges

1. Preheat the oven to 150°C/Gas 2. Place the fish in a large non-stick saucepan, cover with water and poach for 6–8 minutes or until cooked through. Carefully transfer to a non-stick baking sheet and keep warm in the oven.

2. Make the sauce by placing the cucumber, onion and stock in a small saucepan. Bring to the boil, reduce the heat and cook gently for 5–6 minutes.

3. Add the chopped herbs and green chilli, season well and transfer to a food processor. Blend until smooth.

4. To serve, place the poached fish on warmed plates and spoon the sauce over and around them. Serve garnished with wedges of lime.

mediterranean-style
plaice turbans

This is a light and very attractive-looking dish that combines fillets of fresh plaice with a rich, slightly spicy tomato sauce – well worth the time it takes to make the 'turbans'.

SERVES 4

Preparation time

20 minutes

Cooking time

30 minutes

Original: Free

6 spring onions, trimmed and finely chopped

2 garlic cloves, peeled and crushed

1 red pepper, deseeded and finely diced

1 x 400g/14oz can chopped tomatoes

2 tbsp balsamic vinegar

2 tbsp artificial sweetener

2 tsp dried herbs de Provence

salt and freshly ground black pepper

4 plaice fillets, skinned

Fry Light for spraying

to garnish

chopped fresh basil

1. Preheat the oven to 190°C/Gas 5. Place the spring onions in a non-stick frying pan with the garlic, pepper, tomatoes, balsamic vinegar, sweetener and dried herbs. Bring to the boil and cook over a medium heat for 12–15 minutes, stirring often, until the mixture has reduced and thickened. Season.

2. Place the fish fillets on a clean work surface and cut each one in half, lengthways. Carefully spread half the tomato mixture along the surface of the fish. Roll up from the tail end to form a 'turban' and secure with a cocktail stick. Repeat with the remaining fillets.

3. Spray a shallow ovenproof dish with Fry Light and place the rolled 'turbans' of fish in a single layer to fit snugly. Cover lightly with foil and bake in the oven for 10–12 minutes or until the fish is cooked through.

4. To serve, carefully remove the fish from the ovenproof dish and place on warmed plates. Spoon over the remaining tomato sauce, garnish with basil and serve immediately.

parchment fish parcels

Cooking fish in a parcel, or 'en papillote', is a great way to keep in all the juices and flavours – there's no need to add fat, and the aroma when you open the parcel at the table is wonderful.

SERVES 4
Preparation time
20 minutes
Cooking time
25 minutes
Original: Free

8 spring onions, trimmed and finely shredded
1 carrot, peeled and finely julienned
1 red pepper, deseeded and finely sliced
50g/2oz mangetout, very thinly sliced
3 tbsp soy sauce

juice of 2 lemons
1 garlic clove, peeled and finely grated
1 tsp finely grated ginger
4 thick salmon fillets, skinned
salt and freshly ground black pepper

1. Preheat the oven to 200°C/Gas 6. Cut four squares of baking parchment paper, large enough to comfortably wrap each piece of fish.

2. In a large bowl, mix together the spring onions, carrot, red pepper, mangetout, soy sauce, lemon juice, garlic and ginger.

3. Divide this mixture between the four squares of baking parchment and top each one with a salmon fillet.

4. Season well and fold the paper over the fish to form a parcel, with the edges firmly sealed. Place the parcels on a baking sheet and place in the oven for 20–25 minutes or until the fish is just cooked through.

5. Remove from the oven and place the parcels on warmed serving plates. Unwrap the parcels at the table and eat immediately.

comfort food fish pie

Take fish pie to the next dimension by adding broccoli and tomatoes along with a generous mixture of fish and a tasty, comforting topping of creamy mashed swede.

SERVES 4
Preparation time
25 minutes
Cooking time
40 minutes

Original: Free

200g/7oz salmon fillet, skinned
200g/7oz hoki fillet, skinned
Fry Light for spraying
250g/9oz cooked peeled prawns
400g/14oz broccoli florets
2 plum tomatoes, roughly chopped
2 garlic cloves, peeled and crushed
1 egg, beaten
2 tsp mustard powder

2 tbsp Worcestershire sauce
1 tsp Tabasco sauce
4 tbsp chopped chives
4 tbsp chopped flat-leaf parsley
400g/14oz very low-fat natural fromage frais
salt and freshly ground black pepper
1kg/2lb 4oz swede, peeled and roughly chopped

1. Preheat the oven to 220°C/Gas 7. Roughly chop the salmon and hoki fillets into bite-sized pieces and place in a frying pan. Pour over water to cover, bring to the boil, cover and simmer for 5 minutes. Remove from the pan with a slotted spoon and place in a Fry Light-sprayed ovenproof dish together with the prawns.

2. Blanch the broccoli and then drain and add to the fish mixture with the chopped tomatoes. Mix the garlic with the beaten egg. Mix the mustard powder with 1 tbsp water and add to the egg mixture.

3. Stir in the Worcestershire sauce, Tabasco and chopped herbs. Beat in the fromage frais and season well. Pour this mixture over the fish and toss gently to coat evenly.

4. Boil the swede in a large pan of lightly salted water and cook for 12–15 minutes until tender. Drain and mash roughly. Spread the swede mash over the fish mixture and place in the oven and cook for 20–25 minutes until hot and bubbling. Serve immediately.

pasta, rice and grains

couscous with stewed vegetables

couscous
with stewed vegetables

Couscous served with a spicy mix of vegetables is a classic Moroccan dish; the vegetables are very tender and the contrast of taste and texture with the soft, grainy couscous is simple and delicious.

SERVES 4

Preparation time
20 minutes

Cooking time
40 minutes

Green: Free

300g/11oz couscous

Fry Light for spraying

1 onion, peeled and finely chopped

1 tsp ground cinnamon

1 tsp ground ginger

2 tsp ground cumin

2 large carrots, peeled and cut into bite-sized pieces

1 courgette, cut into bite-sized pieces

1 medium aubergine, cut into bite-sized pieces

100g/4oz okra, trimmed

1 red pepper, deseeded and cut into bite-sized pieces

700ml/24fl oz chicken stock made from Bovril

1 x 400g/14oz can chopped tomatoes

1 tbsp artificial sweetener

salt and freshly ground black pepper

to garnish

chopped mint leaves

1. Prepare the couscous according to the packet instructions and keep warm.

2. Spray a large non-stick saucepan with Fry Light and place over a medium heat. Add the onion and the ground spices and stir-fry for 2–3 minutes. Add the vegetables and stir-fry for 2–3 minutes. Pour in the stock, tomatoes and sweetener and bring to the boil.

3. Cover tightly, reduce the heat to medium–low and cook gently for 20–25 minutes, stirring occasionally until the vegetables are tender. Season well.

4. To serve, spoon the prepared couscous into large warmed bowls and spoon over the vegetable mixture. Garnish with the mint leaves and serve immediately.

pasta funghi

Lots of fresh herbs add a wonderful fragrance and flavour to a substantial supper dish made with thick pappardelle pasta.

SERVES 4

Preparation time
15 minutes

Cooking time
20 minutes

Green: Free

350g/12oz dried pappardelle

Fry Light for spraying

1 red onion, peeled and finely diced

2 garlic cloves, peeled and finely chopped

400g/14oz button mushrooms, halved

500ml/18fl oz passata with herbs

1 tbsp artificial sweetener

2 tbsp chopped fresh oregano leaves

2 tbsp chopped fresh flat-leaf parsley

salt and freshly ground black pepper

50g/2oz very low-fat natural fromage frais

1. Cook the pappardelle according to the packet instructions, drain and set aside.

2. Spray a large non-stick frying pan with Fry Light and place over a high heat. Add the onion, garlic and mushrooms and stir-fry for 3–4 minutes.

3. Stir in the passata, sweetener and chopped herbs and bring to the boil. Cover, reduce the heat to low and cook gently for 15 minutes, stirring occasionally. Season well.

4. Just before serving, remove from the heat and stir in the fromage frais to mix well. Divide the pasta between four warmed bowls and top with the sauce.

basil and tomato pesto pasta

The best of Italian cooking is simple, quickly put together and bursting with fresh flavours – just like this delicious combination of a creamy pesto-style sauce coating fine linguine pasta, with juicy ripe tomatoes.

SERVES 4
Preparation time
15 minutes
Cooking time
12 minutes
Green: Free

4 garlic cloves
1 tsp finely grated lemon zest
juice of 1 lemon
8 tbsp very finely chopped fresh basil leaves
200g/7oz Quark soft cheese

salt and freshly ground black pepper
350g/12oz dried linguine
8 midi vine tomatoes, halved or quartered

to garnish
basil leaves

1. Peel and finely grate the garlic to a pulp and place in a food processor with the lemon zest, lemon juice, chopped basil and Quark cheese. Season well and blend until smooth.

2. Cook the linguine according to the packet instructions. When cooked, drain and return to the saucepan.

3. Stir in the pesto mixture and tomatoes and toss to coat evenly.

4. Ladle into warmed pasta bowls or plates, garnish with basil leaves and serve immediately, accompanied by a crisp green salad.

creamy asparagus
carbonara

Carbonara sauce is usually made with ham, but using asparagus instead is a clever way of adding colour and flavour to the dish – and would be especially good in May and June when asparagus is in season.

PASTA, RICE AND GRAINS

SERVES 4
Preparation time
15 minutes
Cooking time
10 minutes

Green: Free

350g/12oz dried linguine or tagliatelle
400g/14oz asparagus tips
2 eggs
100g/4oz very low-fat natural fromage frais

1 garlic clove, peeled and crushed
6 tbsp very finely chopped flat-leaf parsley
salt and freshly ground black pepper
Fry Light for spraying

1. Cook the pasta according to the packet instructions, drain and keep warm.

2. While the pasta is cooking, blanch the asparagus tips in a pan of lightly salted boiling water for 3–4 minutes, or until just tender. Drain and set aside.

3. In a mixing bowl beat the eggs lightly and add the fromage frais and garlic. Whisk until well combined and then stir in the chopped parsley. Season well.

4. Spray a large non-stick frying pan with Fry Light and place over a medium–low heat. Add the pasta and asparagus to the pan and stir and cook for 2–3 minutes until hot. Pour over the 'carbonara' sauce and gently heat through for 2–3 minutes until the pasta is well coated. (Do not allow to boil or the eggs will scramble.) Remove from the heat and serve immediately.

chunky spaghetti bolognese

Everyone loves a 'spag bol' and this one is a classic recipe, except that the minced beef is replaced by Quorn, so that it is Free on a Green day – proving that it is possible to improve on perfection!

SERVES 4

Preparation time
20 minutes

Cooking time
30 minutes

Green: Free

1 onion, peeled and roughly chopped

2 large carrots, peeled and roughly diced

2 sticks of celery, roughly sliced

2 tsp dried mixed herbs

¼ tsp cayenne pepper

4 garlic cloves, peeled and crushed

150ml/5fl oz chicken stock made from Bovril

2 x 400g/14oz cans chopped tomatoes

1 tbsp artificial sweetener

350g/12oz Quorn mince

salt and freshly ground black pepper

350g/12oz dried spaghetti

to garnish
chopped flat-leaf parsley

1. Place the prepared vegetables in a large non-stick frying pan or wok with the dried mixed herbs, cayenne, garlic and stock. Place over a medium heat and bring to the boil. Cook for 3–4 minutes, until the vegetables begin to soften.

2. Stir in the chopped tomatoes, sweetener and Quorn mince. Season well, bring to the boil then cover, reduce the heat and cook gently for 20–25 minutes, stirring often, until the sauce is thick and the vegetables tender.

3. While the sauce is cooking, cook the pasta according to the packet instructions. Drain and keep warm.

4. To serve, divide the cooked spaghetti between four warmed plates and top with the chunky Bolognese sauce. Garnish with chopped parsley and serve immediately.

chilli, chive and beetroot risotto

The flavour of beetroot lends itself very well to a creamy risotto and garnishing it with chilli adds some spicy heat to the mix.

SERVES 4

Preparation time
15 minutes

Cooking time
30 minutes

Green: Free

Fry Light for spraying

1 red onion, peeled and finely chopped

2 garlic cloves, peeled and finely sliced

1 red chilli, deseeded and thinly sliced

500g/1lb 2oz freshly cooked, peeled beetroot

1 small carrot, peeled and finely diced

2 tbsp very finely snipped chives

350g/12oz risotto rice

900ml/1½ pints chicken stock made from Bovril, boiling hot

salt and freshly ground black pepper

4 tbsp very low-fat natural yogurt

to garnish

chives

red and green chilli, deseeded and sliced (optional)

1. Spray a non-stick saucepan or frying pan with Fry Light. Place over a medium heat and add the onion, garlic and chilli and stir-fry for 1–2 minutes.

2. Chop the beetroot into small cubes and add to the pan with the carrots, chives and rice. Add the stock, a ladleful at a time, and cook over a gentle heat for 20–25 minutes, stirring continuously, until all the stock has been absorbed.

3. Season well and ladle into four warmed bowls or plates. Spoon the yogurt over each serving, garnish with chives and chillies, if desired, and serve immediately.

hearty jambalaya

Quorn sausages, rice and lots of vegetables combine to make a quick, yet very filling, casserole with its roots in the American Deep South.

SERVES 4

Preparation time
20 minutes

Cooking time
25 minutes + standing time

Green: Free

1 onion, peeled and finely chopped

2 red peppers, deseeded and roughly chopped

2 sticks celery, thickly sliced

2 garlic cloves, peeled and finely chopped

2 spring onions, trimmed and thinly sliced

1 tsp dried thyme

1 tsp dried oregano

3 large tomatoes

600ml/1 pint chicken stock made from Bovril

1 bay leaf

200g/7oz long grain rice

6 Quorn sausages, roughly chopped

salt and freshly ground black pepper

to garnish
chopped parsley

1. Place the onion, peppers, celery, garlic and spring onions in a large non-stick saucepan. Stir in the dried herbs; roughly chop the tomatoes and add to the saucepan with the chicken stock and bay leaf. Bring the mixture to the boil and add the rice and chopped Quorn sausages. Season well.

2. Bring back to the boil, cover very tightly, reduce the heat to low and allow to cook gently for 15–20 minutes. Remove from the heat and let sit undisturbed for 10–15 minutes.

3. Before serving, fluff up the grains of rice with a fork, and spoon out onto warmed plates or into bowls. Garnish with the chopped parsley and serve immediately.

fragrant spiced vegetable rice

Spicy rice with colourful vegetables is a substantial and moreish dish either on its own or with other Green day Indian dishes, such as spiced potatoes.

SERVES 4

Preparation time
10 minutes

Cooking time
30 minutes + standing time

Green: Free

Fry Light for spraying

1 large onion, peeled, halved and thinly sliced

2 carrots, peeled and diced

1 courgette, trimmed and diced

60ml/2fl oz chicken stock made from Bovril

2 tsp ground coriander

2 tsp cumin seeds

1 tsp ground cumin

¼ tsp crushed cardamom seeds

2 cloves

1 large cinnamon stick

½ tsp ground turmeric

250g/9oz Basmati rice

salt and freshly ground black pepper

1. Spray a large, non-stick frying pan with Fry Light. Place over a medium heat and add the onions, carrots and courgette. Stir and cook for 4–5 minutes and then add the stock and cook for a further 4–5 minutes until most of the stock has been absorbed.

2. Stir in the spices. Stir and cook for 1–2 minutes before stirring in the rice. Stir for a further 1–2 minutes and then pour in 600ml/1 pint water.

3. Season well. Bring to the boil, cover tightly, reduce the heat and cook on a low heat for 12–15 minutes.

4. Remove from the heat and let sit undisturbed for 10–12 minutes before removing the cover. Fluff up the grains with a fork and serve.

singapore-style stir-fry noodles

Plenty of lightly cooked vegetables in this dish ensure it's as healthy as it is tasty; prepare the ingredients before you start stir-frying so that everything cooks together quickly for maximum crunch and flavour.

SERVES 4

Preparation time

15 minutes

Cooking time

20 minutes

Green: Free

2 garlic cloves, peeled and crushed

1 tsp finely grated ginger

1 red onion, peeled and chopped

60ml/2fl oz chicken stock made from Bovril

2 tbsp Worcestershire sauce

2 tbsp dark soy sauce

250g/9oz flat mushrooms, roughly chopped

2 carrots, peeled and finely julienned

1 red pepper, deseeded and thinly sliced

200g/7oz mangetout, thinly sliced

salt and freshly ground black pepper

250g/9oz beansprouts

200g/7oz dried rice noodles

to garnish

chopped coriander leaves

sliced spring onions

1. Place the garlic, ginger, onion, stock, Worcestershire sauce and soy sauce in a large non-stick frying pan. Heat gently and cook over a medium–low heat for 5 minutes.

2. Turn the heat to high and add the mushrooms, carrots, red pepper and mangetout. Stir and cook for 4–5 minutes or until the vegetables are just tender. Season well and stir in the beansprouts and cook for 2–3 minutes.

3. Prepare the noodles according to the packet instructions, drain and add to the vegetable mixture in the pan. Toss to mix well, garnish with chopped coriander and sliced spring onions and serve in bowls with chopsticks.

vegetables

egg, chip and pepper bake

egg, chip and pepper bake

This is a really spectacular dish for a family brunch or supper – the peppers add a marvellous colour and flavour to good old egg and chips.

SERVES 4
Preparation time
10 minutes
Cooking time
35 minutes
Green: Free

1kg/2lb 4oz Desirée potatoes

Fry Light for spraying

1 red pepper, deseeded and thinly sliced

1 yellow pepper, deseeded and thinly sliced

4 large eggs

salt and freshly ground black pepper

to garnish

chopped parsley

1. Preheat the oven to 240°C/Gas 9. Peel the potatoes and cut them into 1cm/½in thick, long chips. Place in a saucepan of boiling water and cook for 4–5 minutes. Drain carefully and spread out on kitchen paper to dry.

2. Place the chips in a shallow medium-sized ovenproof dish or four individual gratin dishes. Spray with Fry Light and bake for 10 minutes. Mix the pepper slices together and add to the potatoes and continue to bake for another 15 minutes, turning occasionally.

3. Remove the dish or dishes from the oven and make four wells in the chip mixture. Break an egg into each well and return to the oven for 5–6 minutes or until the eggs are cooked to your liking. Serve hot, seasoned and sprinkled with chopped parsley.

baby roasted potatoes
with fennel and lemon thyme

Everyone loves roast potatoes and these have the added fragrance and crunch of fennel seeds, garlic salt and lemon thyme – perfect served with fish.

SERVES 4

Preparation time

15 minutes

Cooking time

35 minutes

Green: Free

1.5kg/3lb 6oz baby new potatoes

Fry Light for spraying

2 tsp garlic salt

2 tbsp fennel seeds

4–5 sprigs of lemon thyme

sea salt and freshly ground black pepper

1. Preheat the oven to 220°C/Gas 7. Scrub the potatoes and place in a large pan of lightly salted boiling water and cook for 4–5 minutes. Drain thoroughly.

2. Line a large baking sheet with non-stick baking parchment. Place the potatoes on it in a single layer. Spray with Fry Light. Sprinkle over the garlic salt.

3. Crush the fennel seeds in a pestle and mortar or with a rolling pin, and sprinkle over the potatoes. Scatter over the sprigs of thyme and season well. Place in the oven and roast for 25–30 minutes or until crisp and golden on the outside and soft and tender within. Serve immediately or eat cold in a salad.

spinach
and sweet potato curry

This is a fresh-tasting curry that would be a very satisfying supper served with a pile of steamed Basmati rice, or as part of a delicious Indian buffet.

SERVES 4
Preparation time
15 minutes
Cooking time
18 minutes
Green: Free

300ml/½ pint vegetable stock or chicken stock made from Bovril

750g/1lb 10oz sweet potatoes, peeled and cut into bite-sized wedges

1 onion, peeled, halved and thinly sliced

225g/8oz fresh baby spinach leaves

2 garlic cloves, peeled and thinly sliced

1 red chilli, deseeded and thinly sliced

1 tbsp medium or hot curry powder

4 ripe plum tomatoes, chopped

salt and freshly ground black pepper

1. Place the stock in a large saucepan and add the sweet potatoes and onions. Bring to the boil, reduce the heat, cover and gently cook for 4–5 minutes.

2. Add the spinach, garlic, chilli, curry powder and tomatoes to the saucepan, stir well and cook over a medium heat for 10 minutes or until the spinach has just wilted and the sweet potatoes are tender. Season well and serve hot.

root vegetable,
cabbage and herb mash

Give bubble and squeak an exotic twist by using celeriac and sweet potato, and mixing up the mash with a tangy, creamy dressing. You could use this versatile dish as a topping for vegetable or Quorn cottage pie – or for a hearty winter brunch.

SERVES 4
Preparation time
20 minutes
Cooking time
35 minutes

Green: Free

500g/1lb 2oz sweet potato, peeled and roughly chopped

500g/1lb 2oz celeriac, peeled and roughly chopped

Fry Light for spraying

4 spring onions, trimmed and thinly sliced

300g/11oz green cabbage, thinly shredded

6 tbsp very low-fat natural yogurt

4 tbsp very low-fat natural fromage frais

1 tsp mustard powder

4 tbsp finely chopped flat-leaf parsley

salt and freshly ground black pepper

1. Bring a large pan of lightly salted water to the boil and add the sweet potato and celeriac. Boil for 15–20 minutes or until tender, drain and return to the pan and, using a potato masher, mash roughly. Set aside and keep warm.

2. Spray a large non-stick wok or frying pan with Fry Light and place over a high heat. Add the spring onions and cabbage to the pan and stir and cook for 3–4 minutes. Add 5–6 tablespoons of water, reduce the heat to low, cover tightly and allow to cook gently for 3–4 minutes, stirring occasionally.

3. Stir the cabbage mixture into the root vegetable mash and stir to combine.

4. Beat together the yogurt and fromage frais. Mix the mustard with a tablespoon of water and add to the yogurt mixture. Stir this into the mash and combine well. Scatter over the chopped herbs, season well and serve.

italian-style courgettes

Making courgettes into a very special supper dish or vegetable side-dish is easy with this all-in-one-pan recipe. The creamy onion-flavoured sauce would also work well with pasta.

SERVES 4

Preparation time
15 minutes

Cooking time
12 minutes

Green/Original: Free

Fry Light for spraying

800g/1lb 12oz large courgettes, cut into 1cm/½in slices

1 red onion, peeled, halved and thinly sliced

150ml/5fl oz chicken stock made from Bovril

4 tbsp chopped flat-leaf parsley

2 tbsp finely chopped mint leaves

200g/7oz very low-fat natural fromage frais

salt and freshly ground black pepper

1. Spray a large non-stick saucepan with Fry Light and place over a medium heat. Add the courgette and the onion and stir-fry for 2–3 minutes.

2. Pour in the stock, cover and cook on a gentle heat for 6–8 minutes, stirring occasionally or until the courgettes are just tender.

3. Add the parsley and mint, remove from the heat and stir in the fromage frais. Season well and serve immediately.

braised red cabbage
with red onions

Anyone who doesn't like cabbage will be converted by this wonderfully tasty, warming dish that would be a brilliant accompaniment to cold roast meat or ham, especially at Christmas as it has a festive, spicy taste.

SERVES 4
Preparation time
15 minutes
Cooking time
12 minutes
Green/Original: Free

1.5kg/3lb 6oz red cabbage
2 red onions
Fry Light for spraying
salt and freshly ground black pepper
1 tsp ground cinnamon

3 tbsp red wine vinegar
juice of 1 lemon
3 tbsp artificial sweetener

to garnish
chopped parsley

1. Halve the cabbage, take out the core and then very finely slice into thin shreds. Peel the onions and cut into thin slices.

2. Spray a large non-stick frying pan with Fry Light and place over a high heat. Add the cabbage and onion and stir-fry for 4–5 minutes until the cabbage has softened slightly. Season and add the cinnamon, red wine vinegar and lemon juice.

3. Continue to stir and cook over a high heat for another 5–6 minutes or until the cabbage is just tender but still has a 'bite' to it. Stir in the sweetener and toss to mix well.

4. Remove from the heat and serve, garnished with chopped parsley.

barley and butternut
squash hot pot

Butternut squash is widely on sale in supermarkets and is tasty and easy to cook with. Here it makes a savoury, satisfying stew with a silky texture that comes from the pearl barley.

SERVES 4
Preparation time
15 minutes
Cooking time
1 hour 20 minutes

Green: Free

50g/2oz pearl barley

2 carrots, peeled and cut into thick slices

2 garlic cloves, peeled and crushed

1 bouquet garni

1 litre/1¾ pints chicken stock made from Bovril

800g/1lb 12oz butternut squash, peeled, deseeded and flesh cut into bite-sized pieces

salt and freshly ground black pepper

to garnish

chopped thyme leaves

1. Place the barley in a large saucepan, cover with water and bring to the boil. Cook for 45 minutes or until tender. Drain and return to the saucepan with the carrots, garlic, bouquet garni and stock. Bring to the boil, cover, reduce the heat to medium and simmer gently for 15–20 minutes.

2. Add the butternut squash and continue to cook gently for 10–15 minutes. Season well, discard the bouquet garni and serve immediately, garnished with chopped thyme leaves.

green beans
with puy lentils

Lentils have a nutty, earthy taste that's very moreish. Here they are cooked with spices, tomatoes and fresh, crunchy green beans for a burst of flavour and texture.

SERVES 4
Preparation time
30 minutes
Cooking time
10 minutes
Green: Free

100g/4oz puy lentils, rinsed and drained

400g/14oz fresh green beans, trimmed and halved

Fry Light for spraying

1 onion, peeled and finely chopped

1 garlic clove, peeled and finely sliced

1 tsp finely grated ginger

2 tsp cumin seeds

1 tsp ground coriander

1 red chilli, deseeded and finely sliced

3 tomatoes, roughly chopped

large handful of coriander and mint leaves, chopped

salt and freshly ground black pepper

1. Place the lentils in a large saucepan and cover liberally with cold water. Bring to the boil and cook over a medium heat for 25–30 minutes or until tender. Drain and set aside.

2. While the lentils are cooking, boil the green beans for 8–10 minutes until just tender, drain and set aside.

3. Spray a large non-stick frying pan with Fry Light and place over a medium heat. Add the onion, garlic, ginger, cumin seeds, ground coriander and red chilli. Stir-fry for 2–3 minutes and then add 100ml/3½fl oz water and continue to stir and cook for 3–4 minutes. Add the lentils, beans and tomatoes and cook over a high heat for 2–3 minutes. Stir in the chopped herbs, season and serve immediately.

chunky roasted broccoli
with garlic and herbs

A very fresh and colourful way of cooking broccoli and peppers, this is a versatile dish that would be a filling lunch or a delicious accompaniment to rice or pasta on a Green day, or meat or fish on Original days.

SERVES 4

Preparation time
15 minutes
Cooking time
20 minutes

Green/Original: Free

1kg/2lb 4oz broccoli

Fry Light for spraying

3 red peppers, deseeded and cut into thick strips

6 garlic cloves, peeled and thinly sliced

1 red chilli, deseeded and thinly sliced

salt and freshly ground black pepper

to garnish

a handful of chopped flat-leaf parsley and basil leaves

1. Cut the broccoli into chunky florets. Bring a large saucepan of lightly salted water to the boil. Add the broccoli and boil for 3–4 minutes. Drain and refresh under cold water. Drain and set aside.

2. Preheat the oven to 220°C/Gas 7. Line a large baking sheet with non-stick baking parchment and spray with Fry Light. Place the pepper strips on the prepared baking sheet with the broccoli in a single layer.

3. Scatter the garlic and chilli over the vegetables. Season well and spray the vegetables with Fry Light. Place in the oven and roast for 15–20 minutes. Remove from the oven and transfer to a serving dish with any of the juices. Scatter over the chopped herbs and serve warm or at room temperature.

index